Progress with Oxford

Age ... 5

Addition and Subtraction

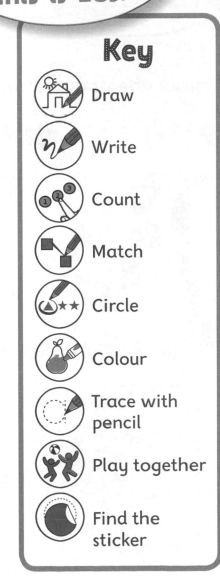

Hello!
I'm Moore and this is Les.

Contents

Key

- Draw
- Write
- Count
- Match
- Circle
- Colour
- Trace with pencil
- Play together
- Find the sticker

OXFORD
UNIVERSITY PRESS

Which is more?

Colour the set that has more.

Count one
then the other.
Which is **more**?

Colour the plate with more cakes.

Colour the dog with more spots.

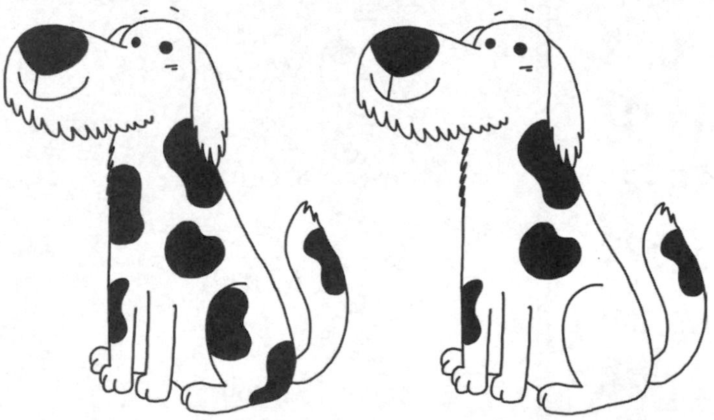

Colour the flag with more stars.

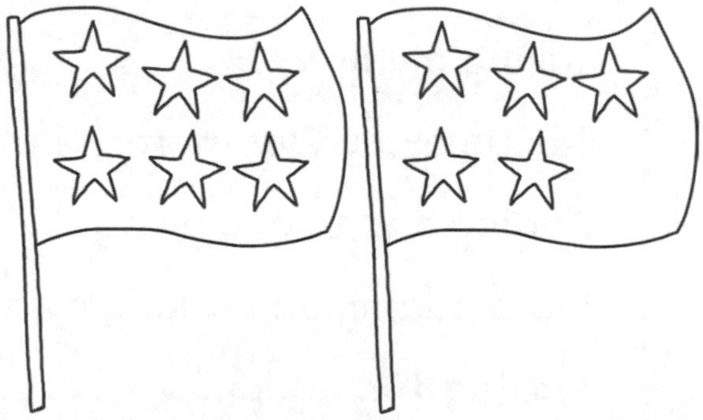

Colour the bowl with more fish.

Colour the necklace with more beads.

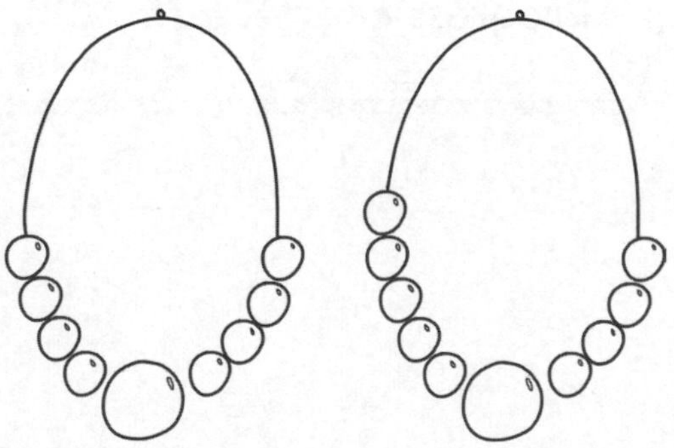

Circle the number that is more.

2 1	1 5
4 3	10 9
5 6	7 8

What else can you count?

Well done!

Give yourself a sticker

Play with counting.

Count the big spoons and little spoons in your kitchen. Which is more?

Use some playing cards (with a value of 2 to 9 only). Pick up a card. Can you think of a number that is more?

Now – track how you're doing on page 32!

Adding 1 more

Draw the same number of objects then add 1 more.

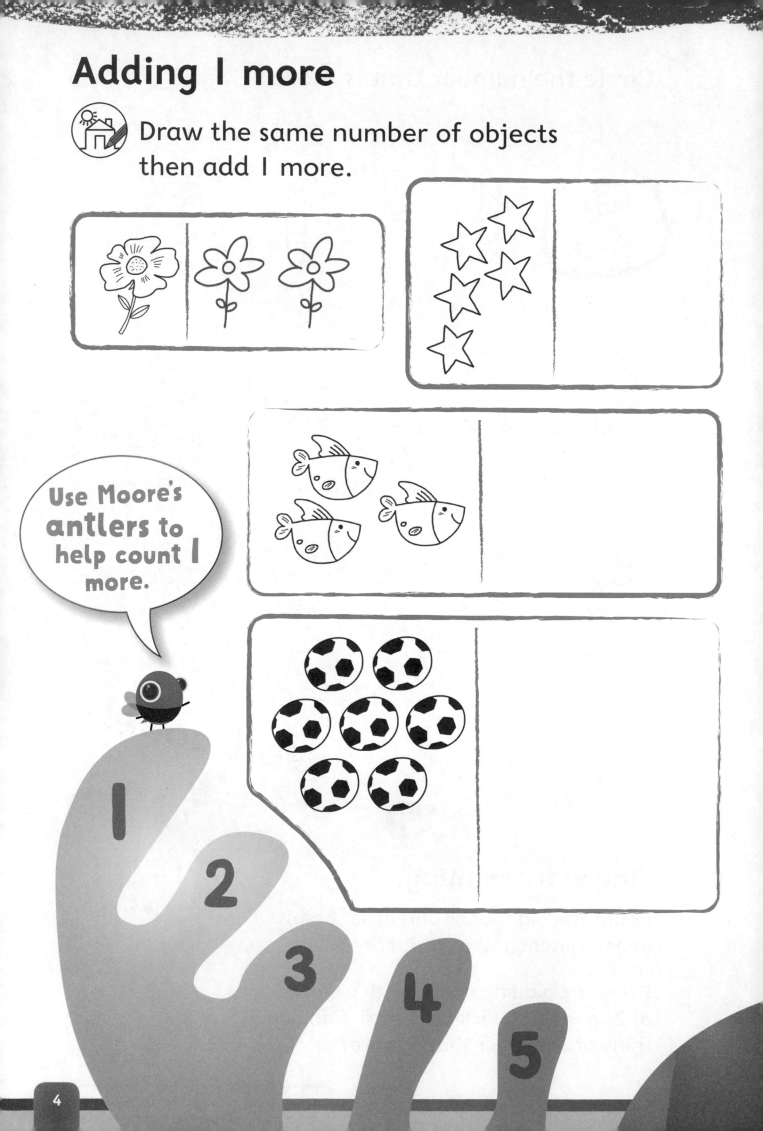

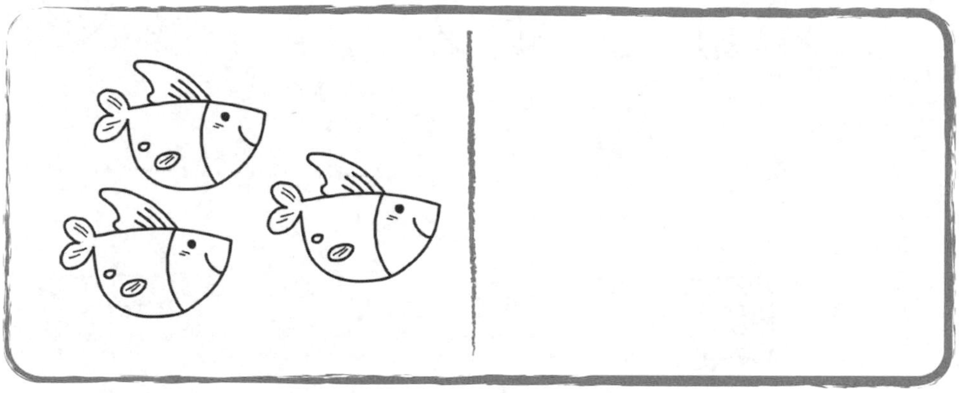

Use Moore's antlers to help count 1 more.
1
2
3
4
5

Draw 1 more.

4

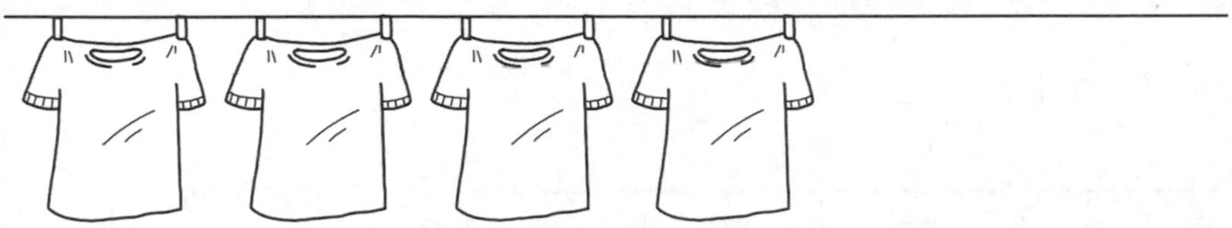

Now – track how you're doing on page 32!

Adding 1 more

Trace the dotted line, just like mine!

Add 1 more using the number line.

Start at 2.

Add 1 more

0 1 2 3 4 5 6 7 8 9 10 makes 3

Start at 4. Add 1 more.

0 1 2 3 4 5 6 7 8 9 10 makes ☐

Start at 3. Add 1 more.

0 1 2 3 4 5 6 7 8 9 10 makes ☐

Start at 7. Add 1 more.

0 1 2 3 4 5 6 7 8 9 10 makes ☐

Start at 0. Add 1 more.

0 1 2 3 4 5 6 7 8 9 10 makes ☐

Start at 9. Add 1 more.

0 1 2 3 4 5 6 7 8 9 10 makes ☐

Start at 6. Add 1 more.

0 1 2 3 4 5 6 7 8 9 10 makes ☐

Add them up and write the answer.

2 add 1 more makes 3

5 add 1 more makes

3 add 1 more makes

8 add 1 more makes

6 add 1 more makes

1 add 1 more makes

9 add 1 more makes

4 add 1 more makes

7 add 1 more makes

You can also write 2 + 1 = 3.

Well done!

Give yourself a sticker

Now – track how you're doing on page 32!

Adding 2 or more

Find the stickers to add more.

Add 2 more.

Add 4 more.

Add 5 more.

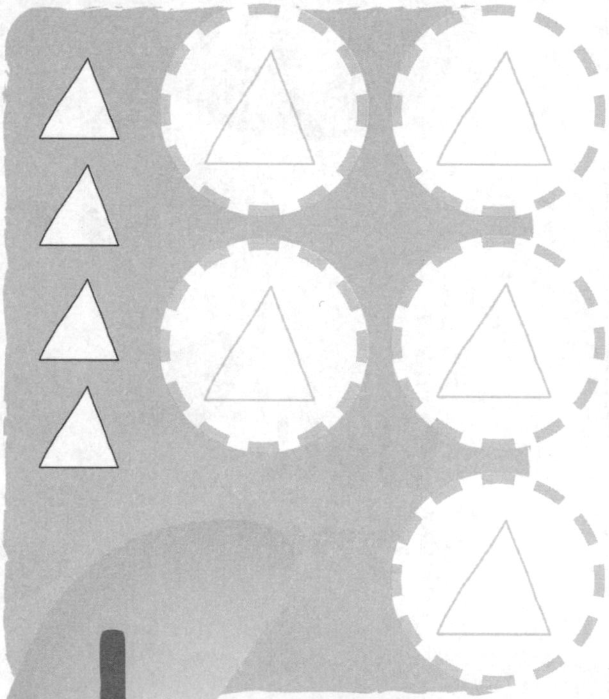

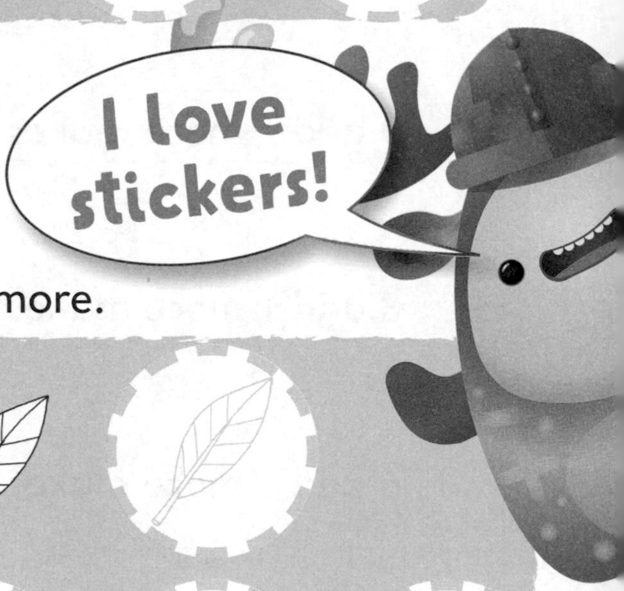

Add 7 more.

Draw the same amount of spots in the box!

Draw more and add them up!

Draw 3 more.

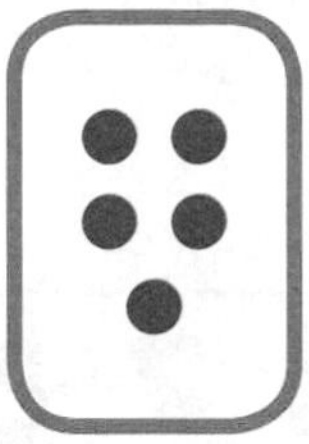

Draw 2 more.

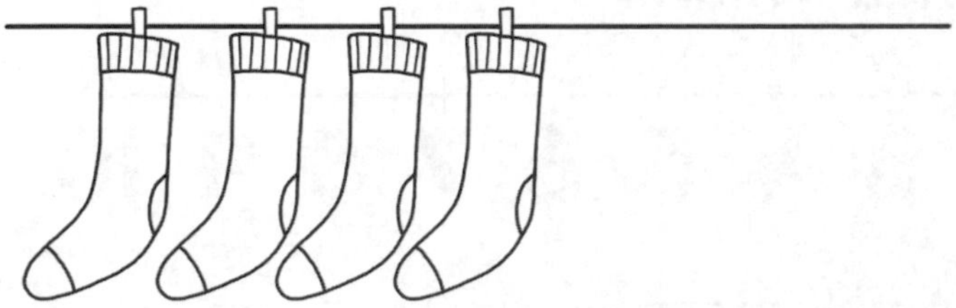

Draw 6 more.

Draw 5 more.

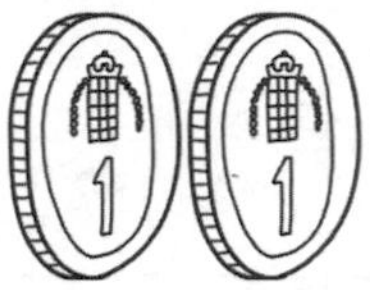

Play with adding.

Draw an alien! Draw 3 more. Draw a spaceship. Draw 4 more. Add them all up.

Say a number from 1 to 5. Ask another person to add 1, 2, 3, 4 or 5 more. Swap.

10
9
8
7
6
Give yourself a sticker

Now – track how you're doing on page 32!

Adding 2 or more

Add more by tracing the dotted lines on the number line.

Start at 1. Add 2 more.

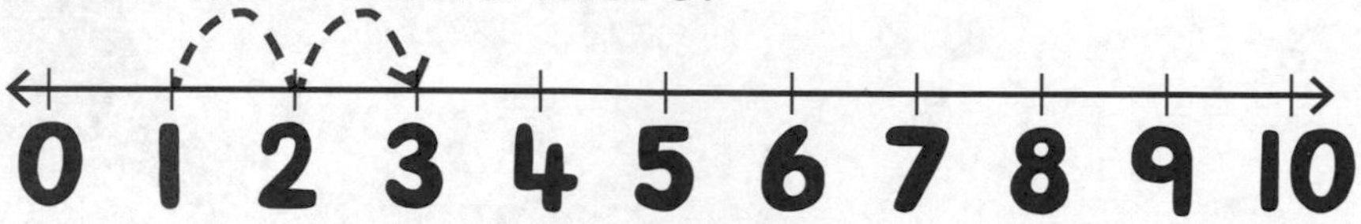

makes

Start at 3. Add 3 more.

makes

Start at 1. Add 4 more.

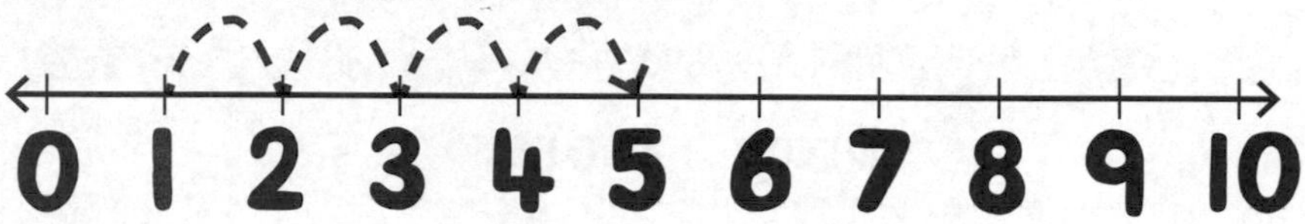

makes

Start at 5. Add 5 more.

makes

Start at 2. Add 6 more.

makes

Start at 2. Add 7 more.

makes

Start at 0. Add 8 more.

makes

Start at 1. Add 9 more.

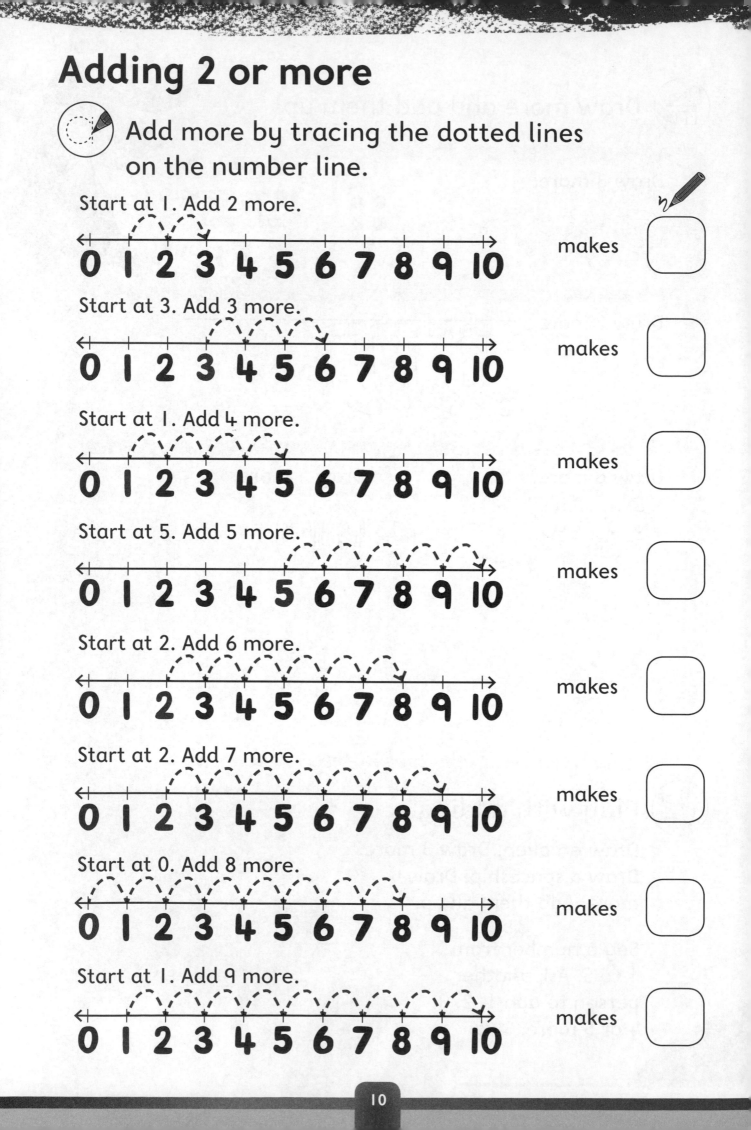

makes

Add them up and write the answer.

1 add 2 more makes ☐

3 add 2 more makes ☐

5 add 3 more makes ☐

1 add 9 more makes ☐

4 add 5 more makes ☐

1 add 6 more makes ☐

8 add 2 more makes ☐

2 add 7 more makes ☐

You could draw a number line from 0 to 10 to help you count on.

The + symbol means add.

Well done!

Give yourself a sticker

Play with adding.

Count the number of doors in your home. Count the number of windows. Add them together.

Play with a friend and each roll 2 dice. Add the numbers up. Who got more?

Now – track how you're doing on page 32!

Which is less?

Colour the set that has less.

Fewer means the same as less

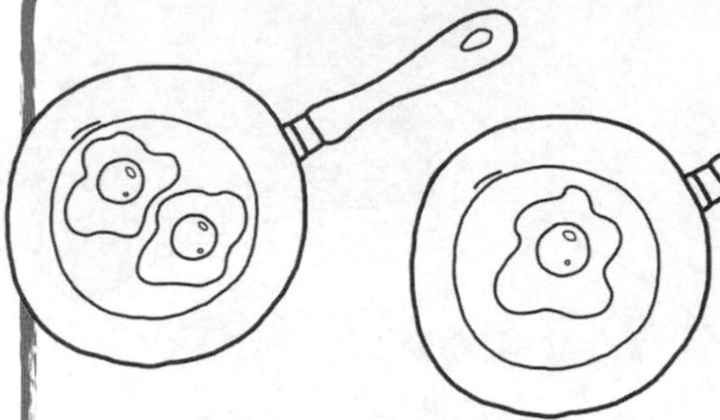

Which is less? Colour the pan with fewer eggs.

Colour the ladybird with fewer spots.

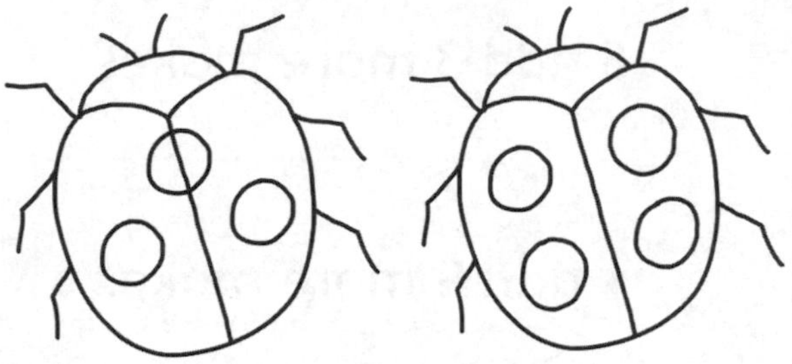

Colour the sock with fewer stars.

Colour the kite with fewer bows.

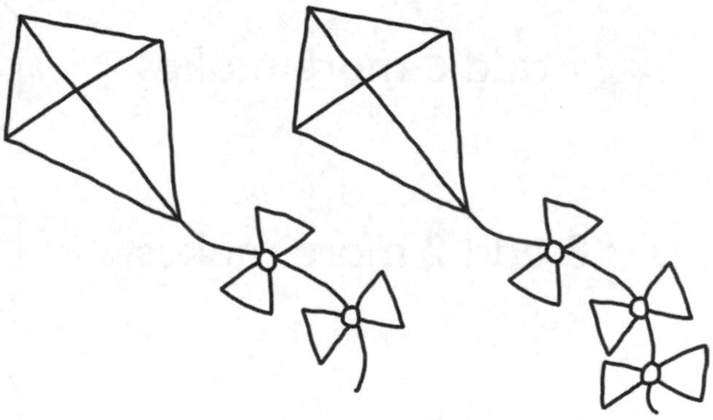

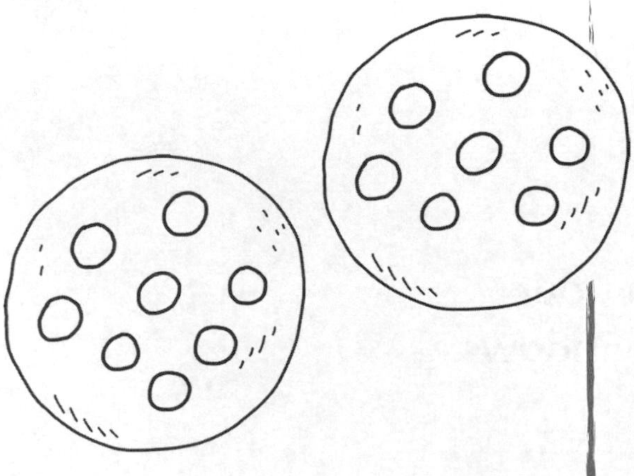

Colour the biscuit with fewer chocolate chips.

Colour the face with fewer teeth.

Circle the number that is less.

3 4	2 1
6 5	9 10
7 8	4 3

Well done!

Give yourself a sticker

Now – track how you're doing on page 32!

Taking away 1

Cross 1 animal out.

Write how many are left.

1 left

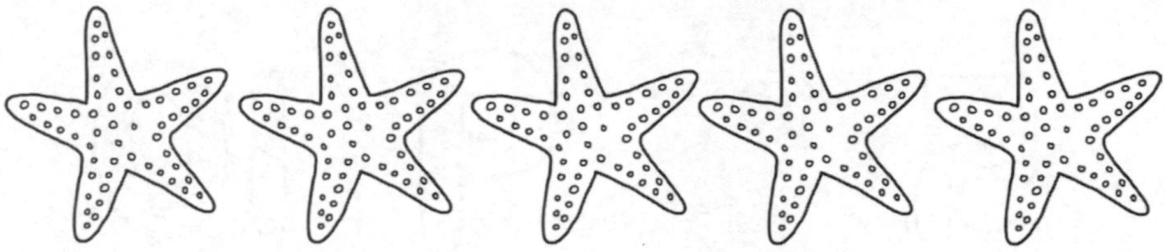

left

left

left

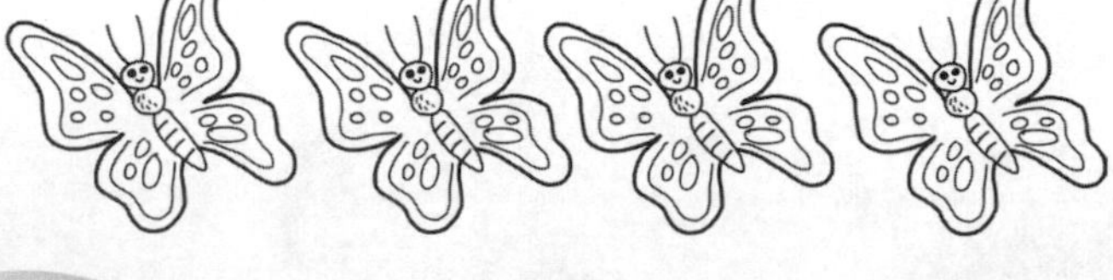

left

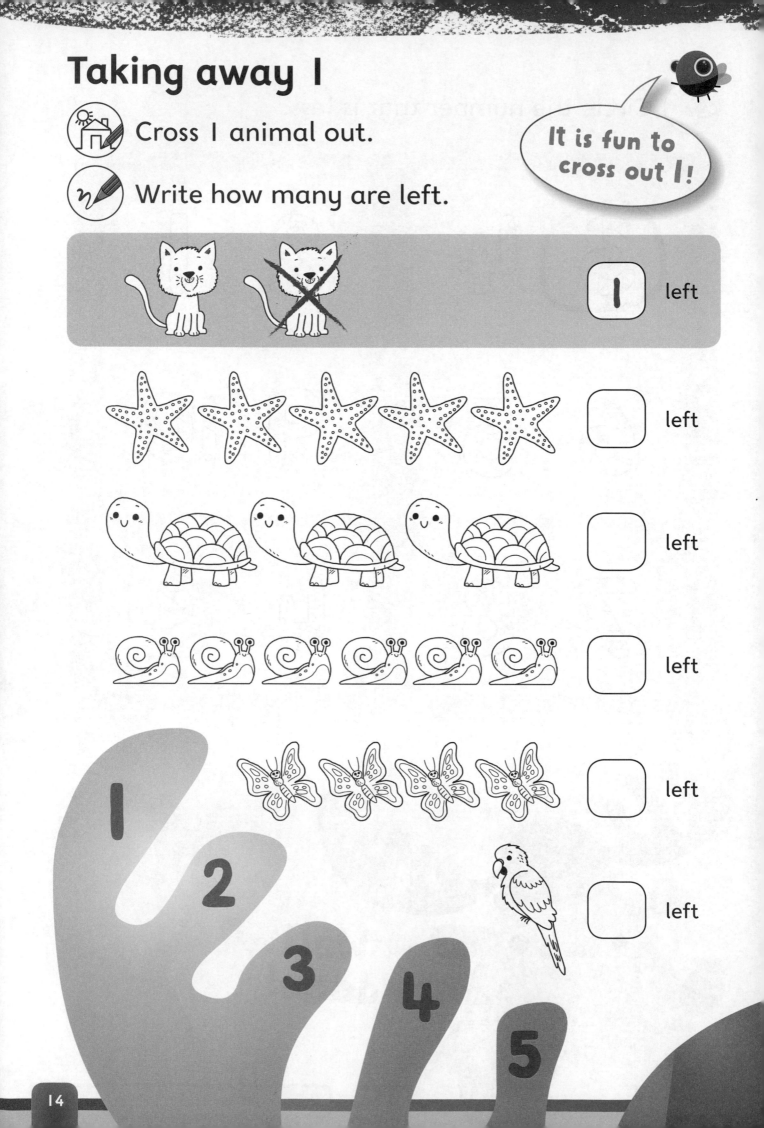

left

1 2 3 4 5

Copy the picture but take away 1 spot.

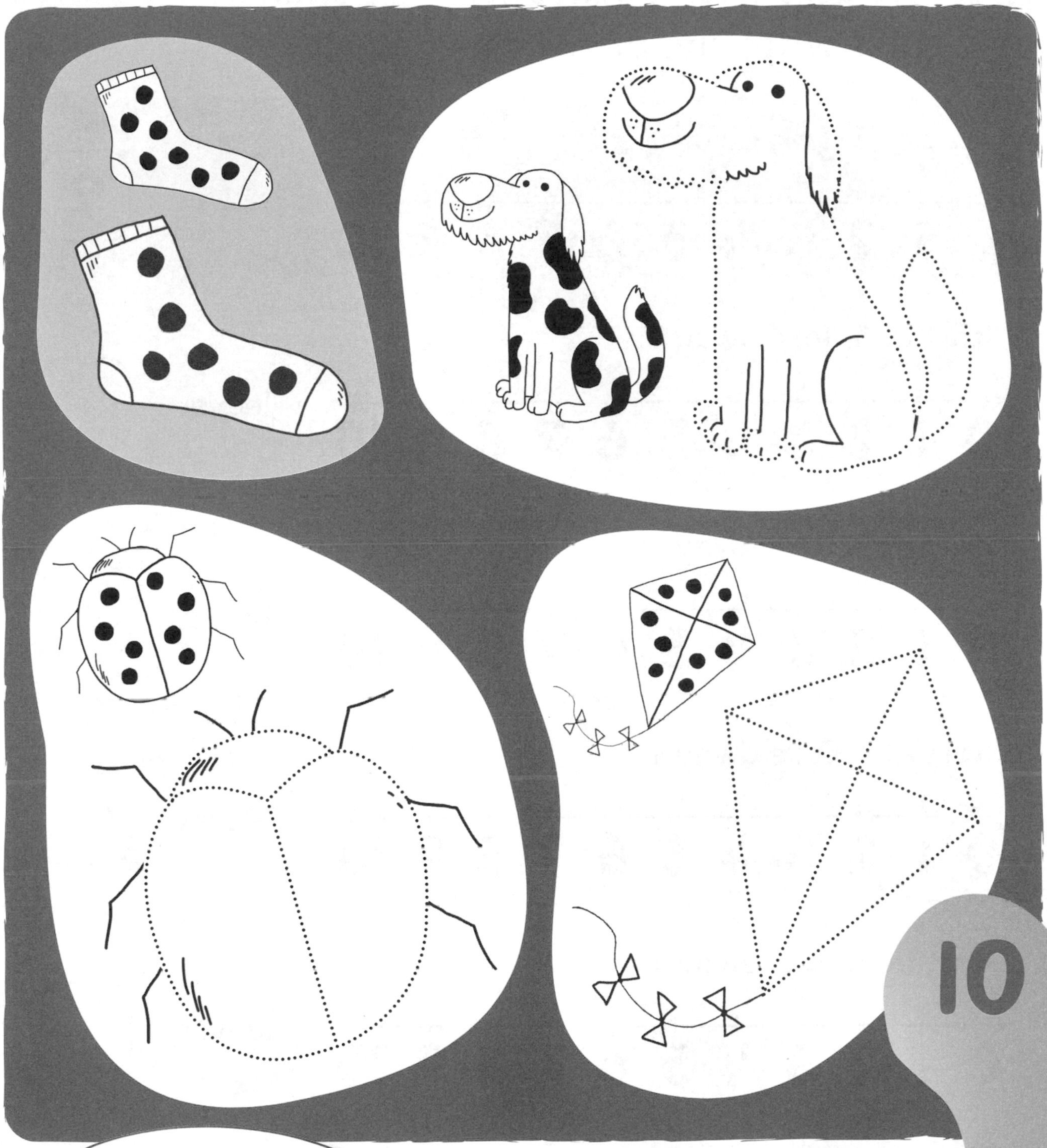

Use the number line to count 1 less.

Now – track how you're doing on page 32!

Taking away 1 number

What is 1 less? Trace with a pencil and write the answer.

Start at 3. Take away 1.

0 1 2 3 4 5 6 7 8 9 10 leaves 2

Start at 5. Take away 1.

0 1 2 3 4 5 6 7 8 9 10 leaves

Start at 9. Take away 1.

0 1 2 3 4 5 6 7 8 9 10 leaves

Start at 1. Take away 1.

0 1 2 3 4 5 6 7 8 9 10 leaves

Start at 7. Take away 1.

0 1 2 3 4 5 6 7 8 9 10 leaves

Start at 10. Take away 1.

0 1 2 3 4 5 6 7 8 9 10 leaves

The dotted line will help you.

Stickers for page 8

Character stickers

Reward Stickers

Take away 1.

5 take away 1 leaves ☐

3 take away 1 leaves ☐

8 take away 1 leaves ☐

2 take away 1 leaves ☐

7 take away 1 leaves ☐

4 take away 1 leaves ☐

10 take away 1 leaves ☐

9 take away 1 leaves ☐

6 take away 1 leaves ☐

You can also write 3 − 1 = 2.

Play with counting back.

Make a model spaceship. Count backwards from 10 to 'Lift off!'

Learn the song *Ten Green Bottles*.

Play Snakes and Ladders with a friend.

Give yourself a sticker

Now – track how you're doing on page 32!

Taking away 2 or more

Cross out the correct amount and write how many are left.

Cross 2 out.

2 left

Cross 4 out.

☐ left

Cross 6 out.

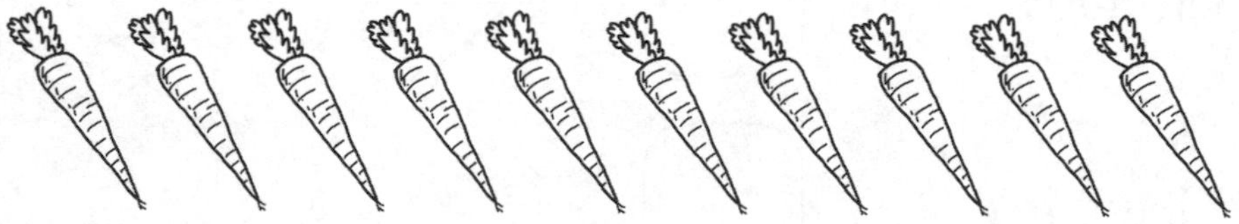

☐ left

Cross 5 out.

☐ left

Cross 3 out.

☐ left

Cross 7 out.

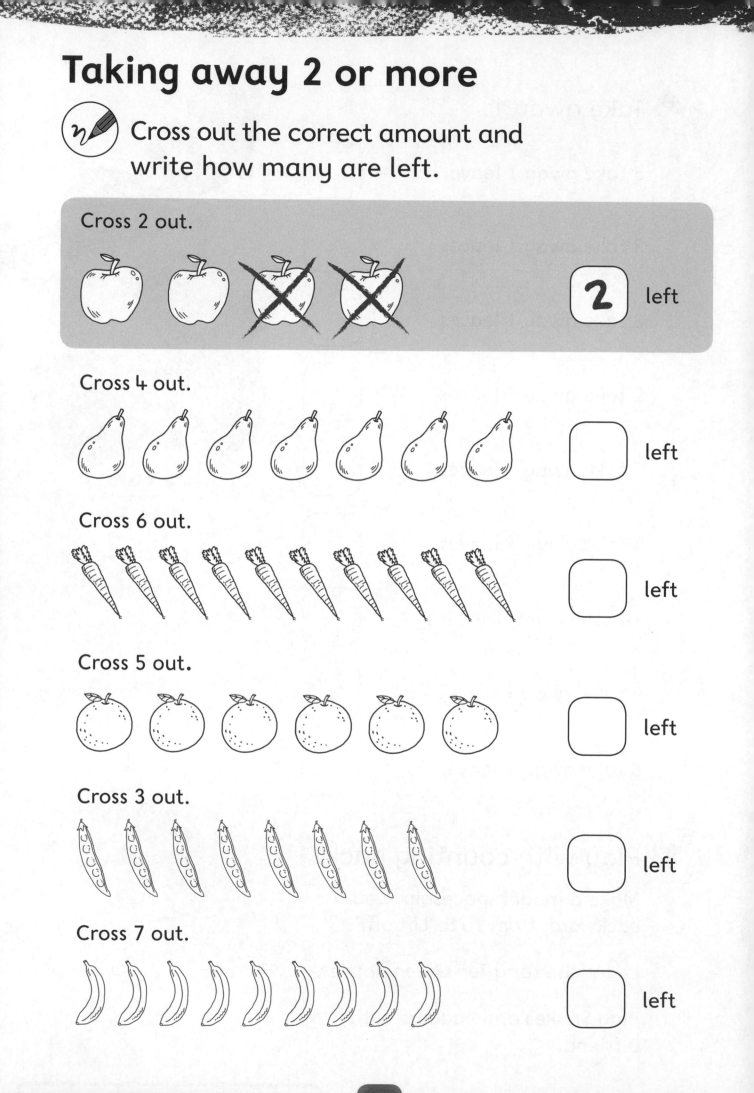

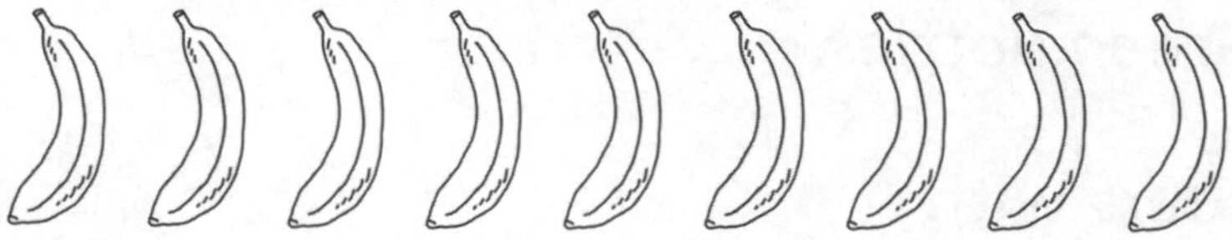

☐ left

Take away the spots and draw how many there are left.

Take away 2 spots.

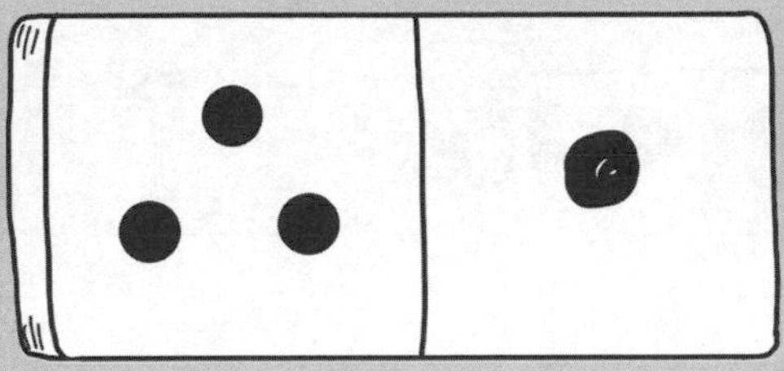

1 left

Take away 2 spots.

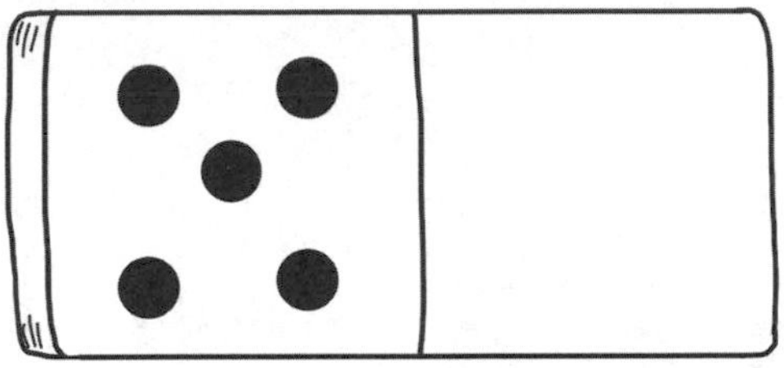

left

Take away 3 spots.

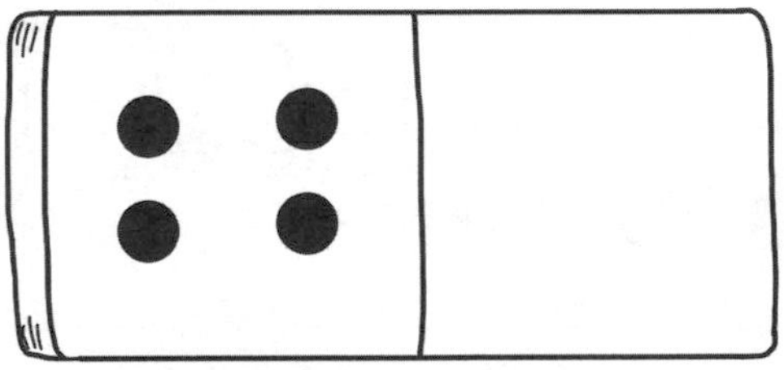

left

Take away 4 spots.

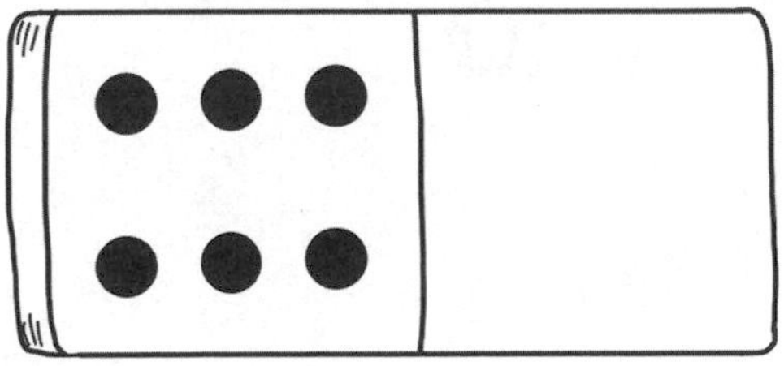

left

Give yourself a sticker

Take away 5 spots.

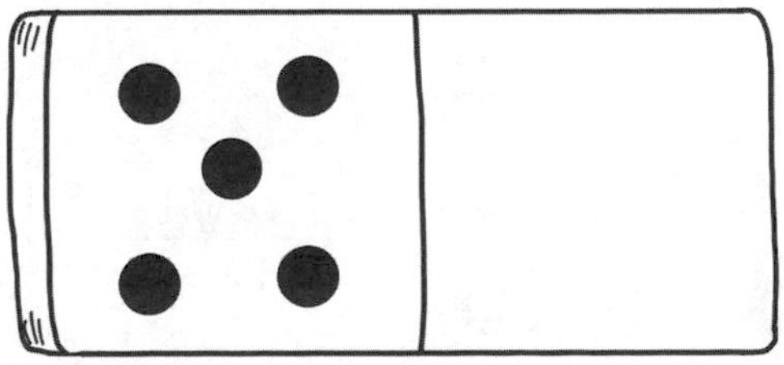

left

Now – track how you're doing on page 32!

Taking away 2 or more

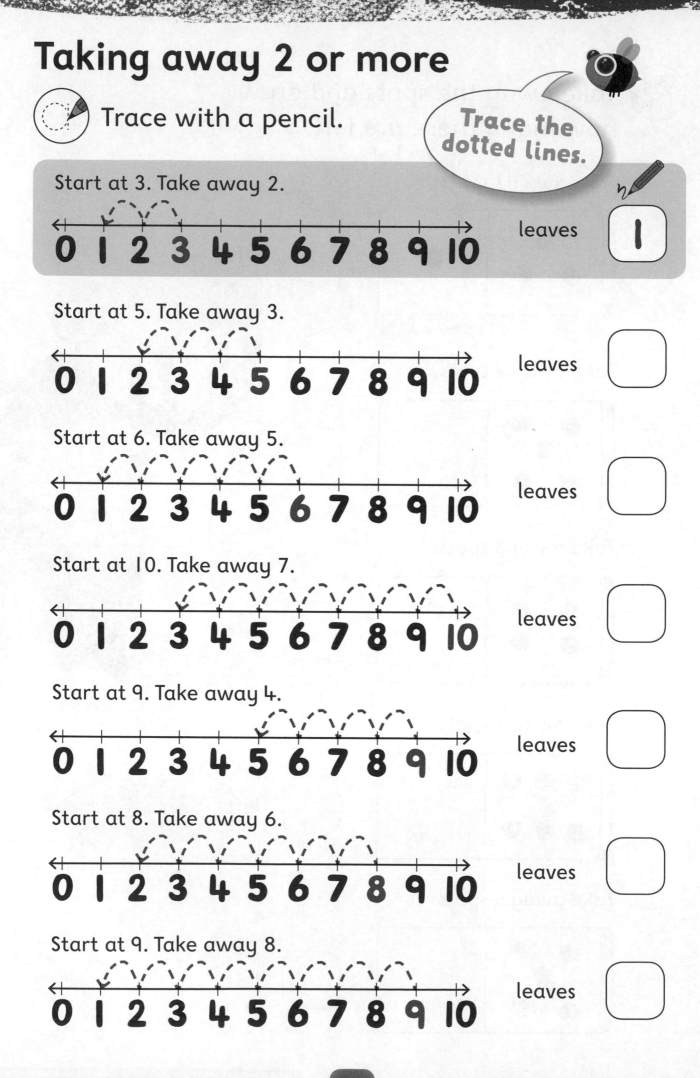

Trace the dotted lines.

Trace with a pencil.

Start at 3. Take away 2.

0 1 2 3 4 5 6 7 8 9 10

leaves 1

Start at 5. Take away 3.

0 1 2 3 4 5 6 7 8 9 10

leaves

Start at 6. Take away 5.

0 1 2 3 4 5 6 7 8 9 10

leaves

Start at 10. Take away 7.

0 1 2 3 4 5 6 7 8 9 10

leaves

Start at 9. Take away 4.

0 1 2 3 4 5 6 7 8 9 10

leaves

Start at 8. Take away 6.

0 1 2 3 4 5 6 7 8 9 10

leaves

Start at 9. Take away 8.

0 1 2 3 4 5 6 7 8 9 10

leaves

Take it away!

Draw a number line from 0 to 10 to help you count back.

3 take away 2 leaves ☐

10 take away 3 leaves ☐

9 take away 6 leaves ☐

6 take away 4 leaves ☐

10 take away 4 leaves ☐

9 take away 5 leaves ☐

8 take away 3 leaves ☐

7 take away 2 leaves ☐

5 take away 1 leaves ☐

The – symbol means take away.

Play with taking away.

Lay out 10 toys. Get a friend to take some of the toys away. How many are left?

Roll 2 dice. Take the smaller number away from the larger number.

Give yourself a sticker

Now – track how you're doing on page 32!

Adding and taking away

Add or take away using the number line.

Start at 5. Add 3 more.

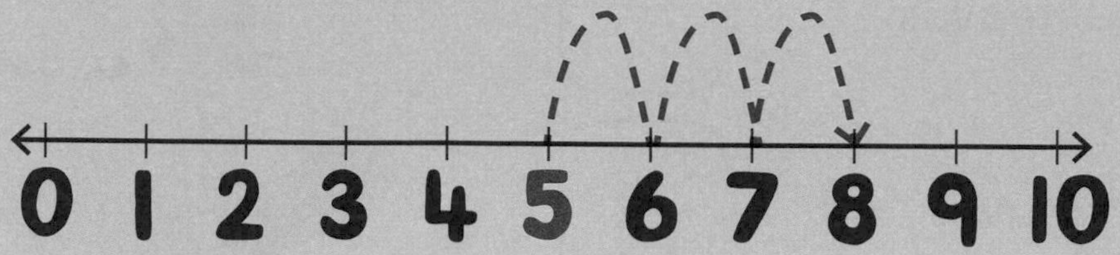

makes 8

Start at 3. Add 4 more.

makes

Start at 4. Take away 2.

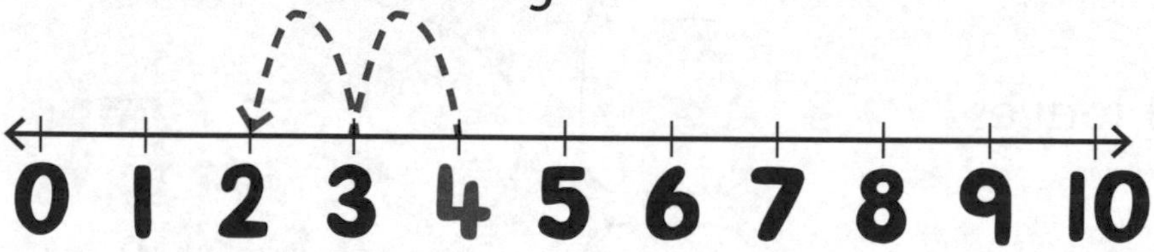

leaves

Start at 7. Add 3 more.

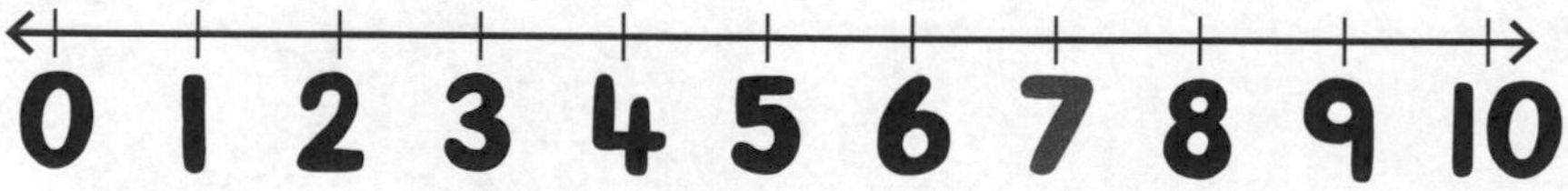

makes

Start at 8. Take away 5.

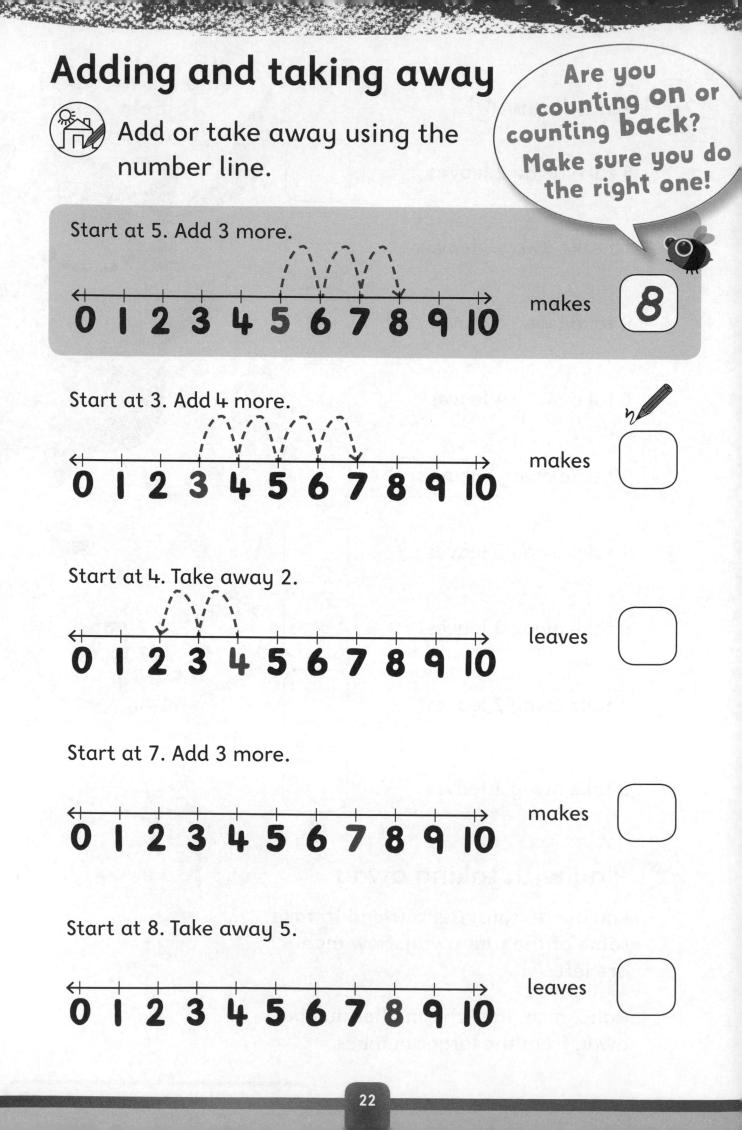

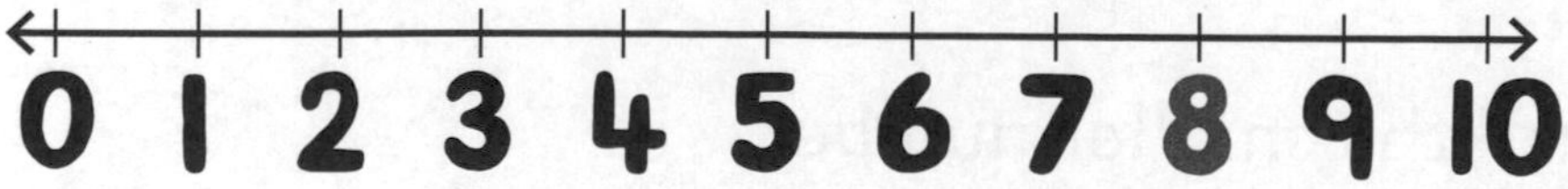

leaves

Add or take away using the number line.

Start at 5. Take away 4.

0 1 2 3 4 5 6 7 8 9 10

leaves ☐

Start at 1. Add 3 more.

0 1 2 3 4 5 6 7 8 9 10

makes ☐

Start at 9. Take away 3.

0 1 2 3 4 5 6 7 8 9 10

leaves ☐

Start at 10. Take away 5.

0 1 2 3 4 5 6 7 8 9 10

leaves ☐

Start at 3. Add 6 more.

0 1 2 3 4 5 6 7 8 9 10

makes ☐

Give
yourself
a sticker

Now – track how you're doing on page 32!

More adding and taking away

Count on or back using the number line.

Write the answer.

2 + 1 = ☐	6 + 2 = ☐
3 – 2 = ☐	7 – 3 = ☐
4 + 3 = ☐	8 + 2 = ☐
5 – 4 = ☐	9 – 5 = ☐

The + means add and the – means take away
The = means the same as or equals to
1
2
3
4
5

Write the missing number.

Use the number line to help you out.

2 – ☐ = 1	6 – ☐ = 1
3 + ☐ = 7	7 + ☐ = 9
4 – ☐ = 2	8 – ☐ = 4
5 + ☐ = 8	9 + ☐ = 10

I love playing games!

Check the sign! Is it + or – ?
10
9
8
7
6
Give yourself a sticker

Play with adding and taking away.

Choose a number between 0 and 4. Roll a dice. Add the numbers up.

Choose a number between 6 and 10. Roll a dice. Take that number away.

Now – track how you're doing on page 32!

Making 10

Draw more to make 10!

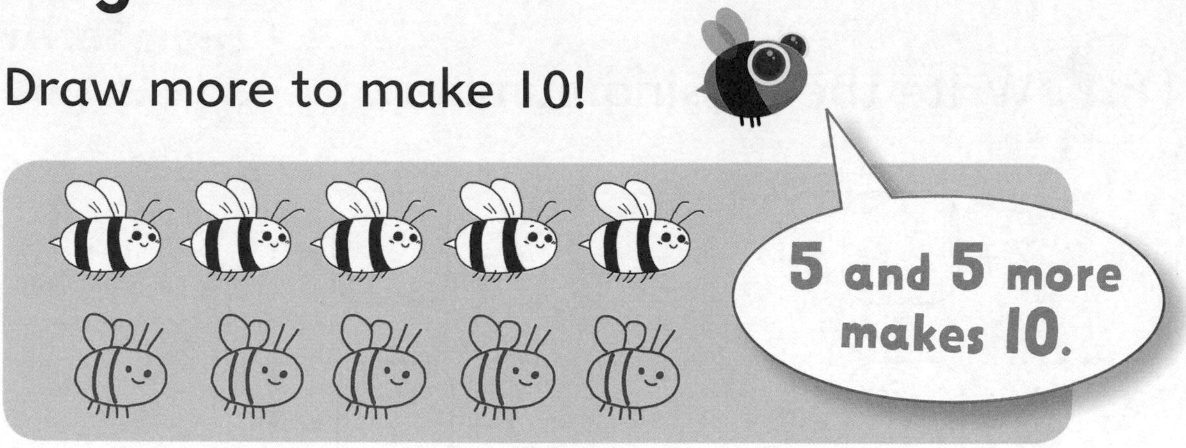
5 and 5 more makes 10.

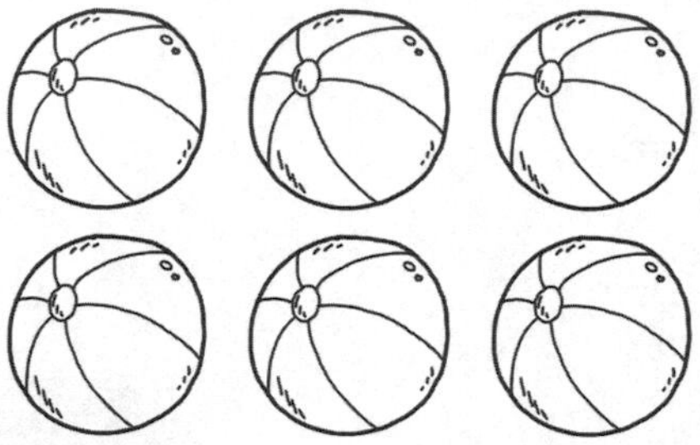

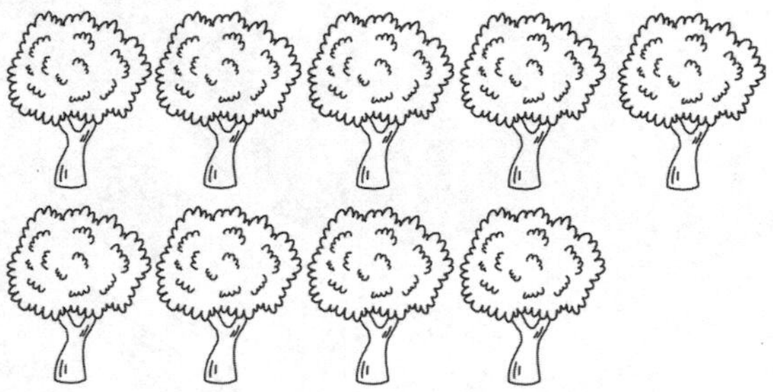

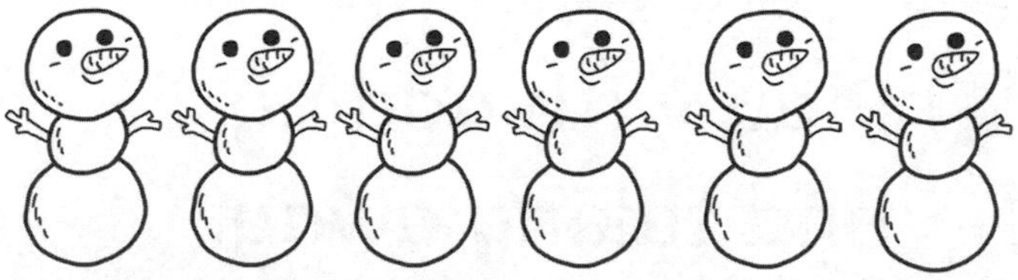

How many more makes 10? Write the missing number.

5 and ___ more makes 10.

8 and ___ more makes 10.

6 and ___ more makes 10.

9 and ___ more makes 10.

4 and ___ more makes 10.

7 and ___ more makes 10.

2 and ___ more makes 10.

3 and ___ more makes 10.

1 and ___ more makes 10.

These are called number bonds to 10.

Play with making numbers up to 10.

Write a number between 1 and 5. Tell someone else to write a number between 5 and 9. Do both numbers make 10?

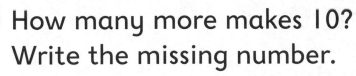

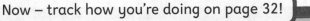

Give yourself a sticker

Now – track how you're doing on page 32!

Counting more than 10

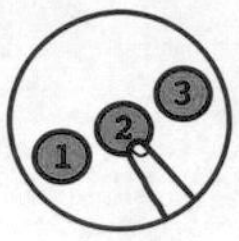

Count on using the number line.

Start at 8. Add 3 more.

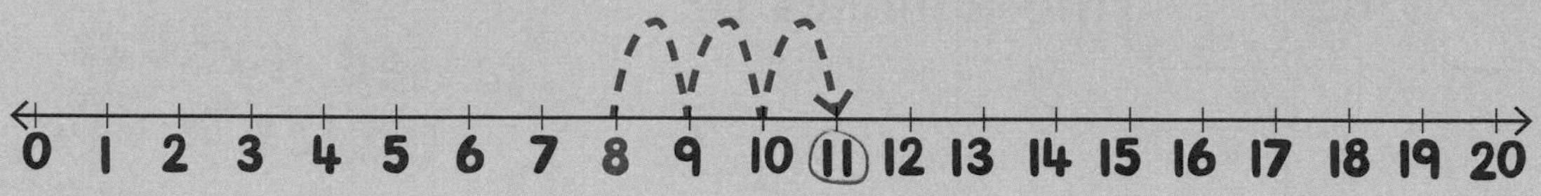

11

Start at 7. Add 5 more.

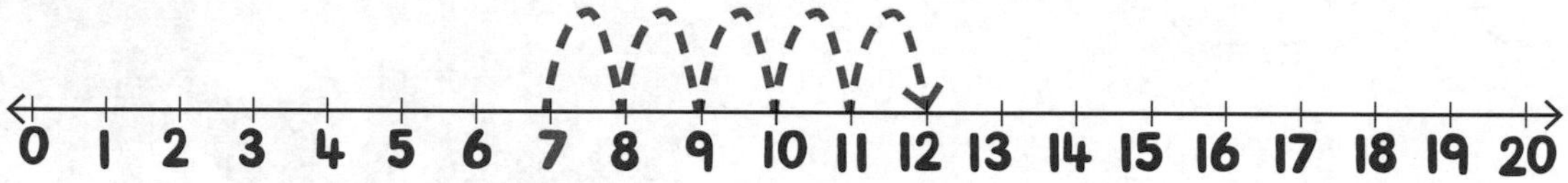

Start at 9. Add 4 more.

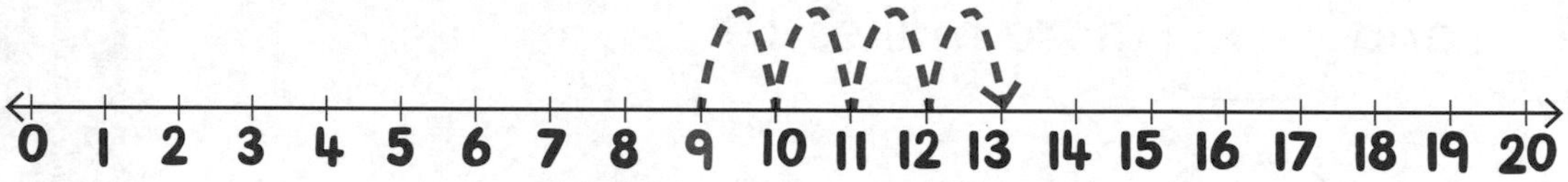

Start at 6. Add 6 more.

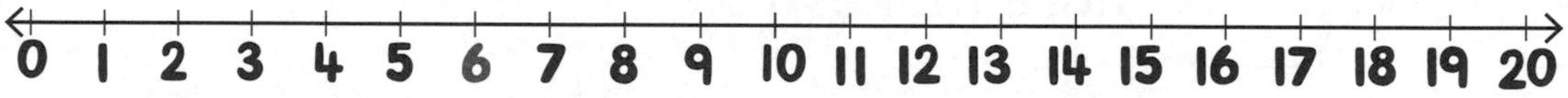

Start at 9. Add 8 more.

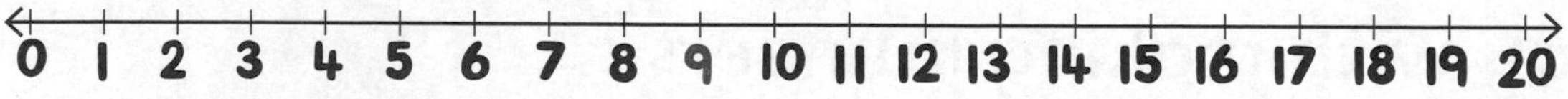

Start at 7. Add 9 more.

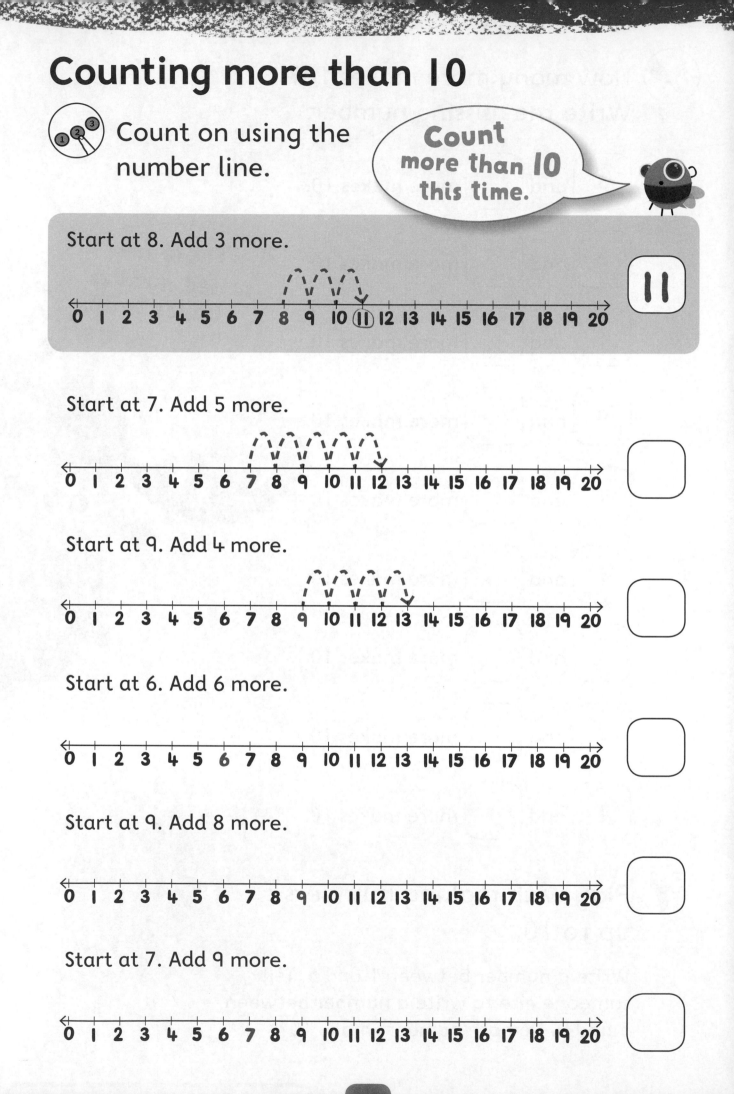

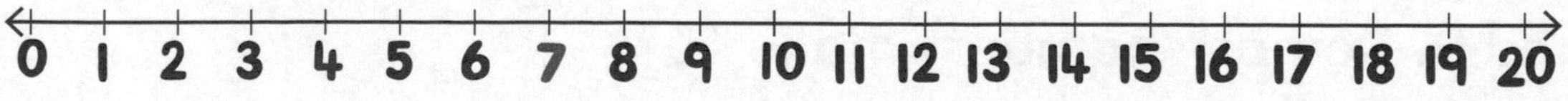

Add them up and write the answer.

Put the first number in your head and count on.

8 + 4 = ☐	7 + 6 = ☐
9 + 2 = ☐	8 + 9 = ☐
6 + 8 = ☐	7 + 5 = ☐
7 + 9 = ☐	6 + 9 = ☐
8 + 7 = ☐	7 + 4 = ☐
9 + 4 = ☐	9 + 5 = ☐

Play with adding.

Write the numbers 1 to 9 on separate pieces of paper. Turn the pieces over to hide the numbers. Pick 2 pieces of paper and add the numbers together.

Find some coins and choose 3. Add them together. Add another. How much now? Keep going.

Give yourself a sticker

Now – track how you're doing on page 32!

Making doubles

'Double 2' means '2 and 2 more'.

Draw the same number of spots on the other side and add them up.

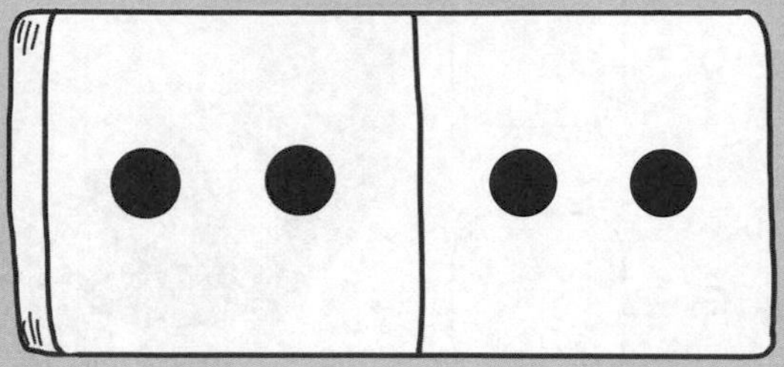

makes 4

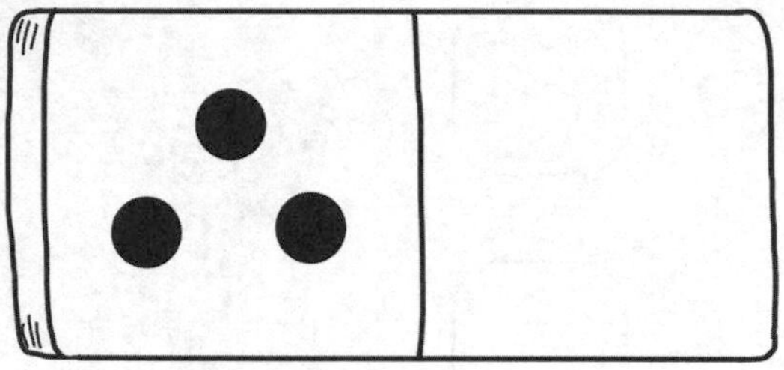

makes ☐

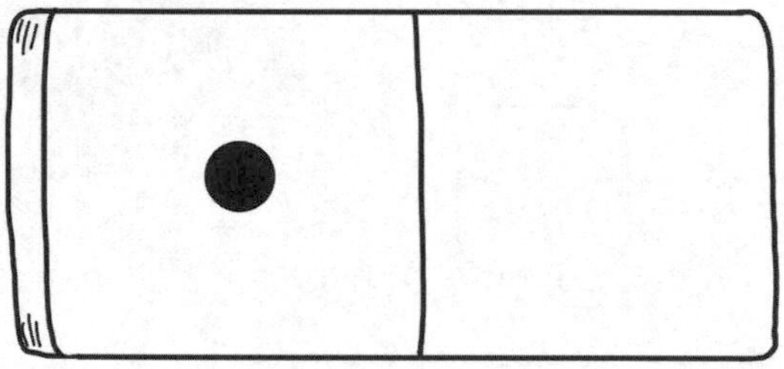

makes ☐

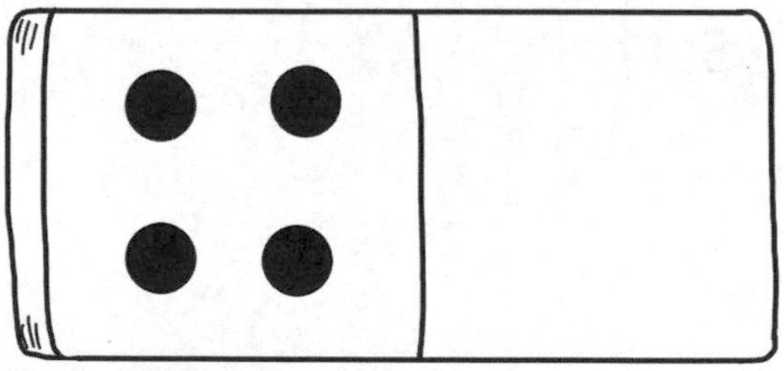

makes ☐

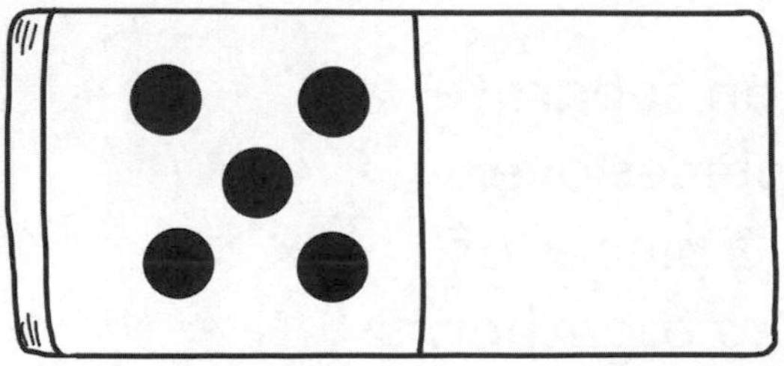

makes ☐

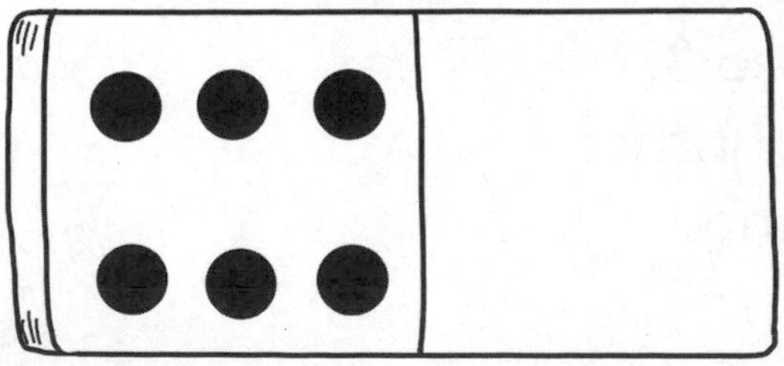

makes ☐

Draw a line to match the numbers.

double 2	6
double 1	4
double 3	10
double 5	2
double 6	12
double 4	18
double 7	8
double 9	16
double 8	14

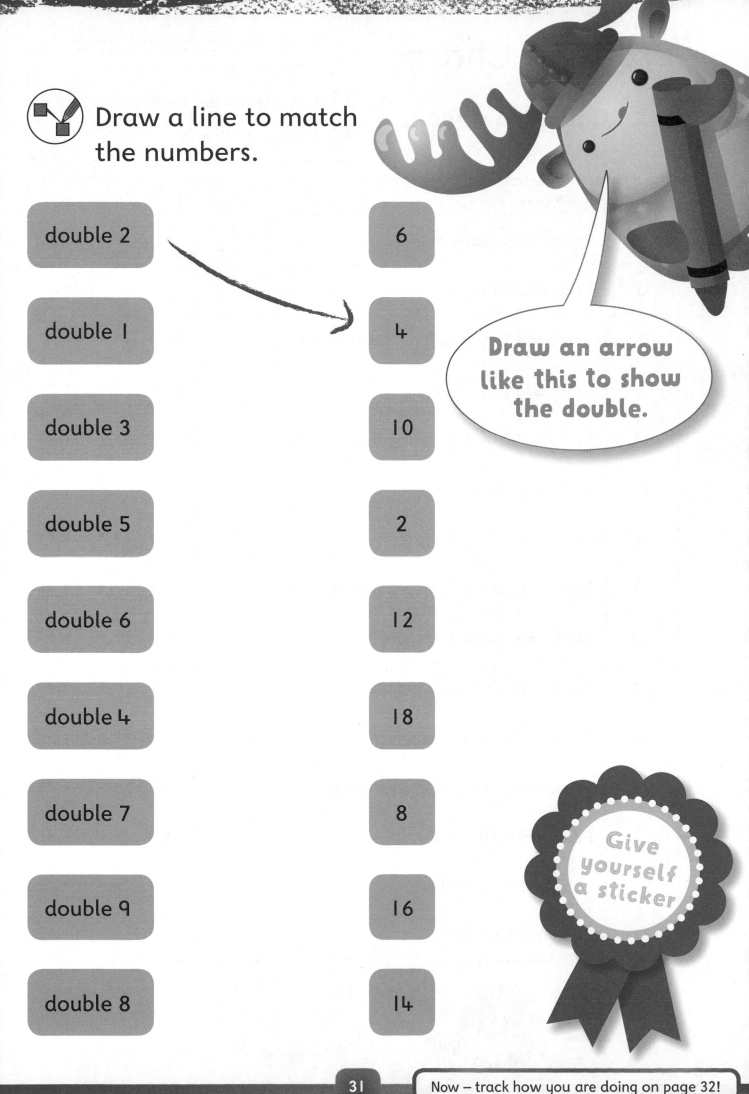

Draw an arrow like this to show the double.

Give yourself a sticker

Now – track how you are doing on page 32!

Progress Chart

Colour in a face.

- I can do this well
- I can do this but need more practice
- I find this difficult

Page	I can . . .	How did you do?
3	I can say which is more.	
5	I can add 1 more.	
7	I can add 1 more using a number line.	
9	I can add 2 or more.	
11	I can add 2 or more using a number line.	
13	I can say which is less.	
15	I can take away 1.	
17	I can take away 1 using a number line.	
19	I can take away 2 or more.	
21	I can take away 2 or more using a number line.	
23	I can add or take away using a number line.	
25	I can add or take away using numbers.	
27	I can make 10.	
28	I can make more than 10.	
31	I can make doubles.	

How did YOU do?